A STORYBOOK TO COLOR

IT'S ANOTHER HOLIDAY, CHARLIE BROWN

CHARLES M. SCHULZ

Copyright © 1977 by United Feature Syndicate, Inc. Based upon the books *Be My Valentine, Charlie Brown* (Copyright © 1976 by United Feature Syndicate, Inc.), *It's Arbor Day, Charlie Brown* (Copyright © 1977 by United Feature Syndicate, Inc.), *It's the Easter Beagle, Charlie Brown* (Copyright © 1976 by United Feature Syndicate, Inc.), *A Charlie Brown Thanksgiving* (Copyright © 1974 by United Feature Syndicate, Inc.) and *A Charlie Brown Christmas,* (Copyright © 1977 by United Feature Syndicate, Inc.).

All rights reserved under International and Pan-American Copyright Conventions. Published in the United States by Random House, Inc., New York. Library of Congress Catalog Card Number: 79-89724 ISBN: 0-394-62212-X This edition published by arrangement with Random House, Inc. Manufactured in the United States of America 9 8 7 6 5 4 3 2 1 Random House Student Book Club Edition: First Printing, 1979

Random House/New York

Who will get
Linus's heart?

See page 8.

What's a tree doing in the middle of Charlie Brown's pitcher's mound?

See page 28.

Is this any way
to make Easter eggs?

See page 48.

It's Thanksgiving!

Where's the turkey? Where's the cranberry sauce?
Where's the pumpkin pie?

See page 64.

Who has the true Christmas spirit?

Lucy?

or Snoopy?

or Charlie Brown?

See page 84.

Be My Valentine,

Charlie Brown

I think I could spend my whole life by the mailbox and still never get a valentine.

Valentine? That's what I'll get my teacher, Miss Othmar. I feel so strongly about her that I'll get her the biggest valentine there is.

If you're buying that for Miss Othmar, Linus, you'd better be careful. It's not a good idea to fall in love with your teacher.

Linus's valentine for Miss Othmar

Did you see that? Did you see what Linus bought for me for a Valentine's Day present? Fantastic! I'll have to get him a good present, too.

I'm trying to make Linus a valentine. I've got to give him something that is just as good as the candy he bought me.

Here's the valentine
I'd *like* to make for
my lover boy.

15

The Class Valentine's Day Party

O.K. Everybody put your valentines in this box.

I can't get my valentine in the box. I'll have to give it personally.

O.K. Now I'll give out the valentines. Here's one for Sally. And one for Frieda. One for Monte. One for Lucy. And one for Violet. One big one for Tom. One for Peppermint Patty. One for Franklin. And one for Linus. One for Pig-Pen. One for Amy. Another one for Frieda. Here's one for Jill. And here's one . . .

19

Look at that! Charlie Brown still hasn't received a valentine.
I guess no one wants to waste one on him.

Sigh! All the valentines were given out. The box is empty, and I never got even one.

Here comes Linus with my box of candy. This is my big moment. I think I'll pucker up.

I'd better hurry and give Miss Othmar her Valentine's present before she leaves.

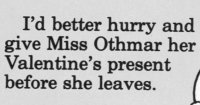

If you're looking for Miss Othmar, she's gone.
She left a minute ago for the parking lot.

There goes Linus! He's running to the parking lot! To Miss Othmar's car! With *my* box of candy!!! And there's Miss Othmar with her boyfriend!

There's nothing to do now but dump this box of candy in the river.

The next day . . .

Charlie Brown, we've been feeling awfully guilty about
not giving you a valentine this year. So, here, I've erased
my name from this one. I'd like you to have it.

I'll take it! Happy Valentine's Day!

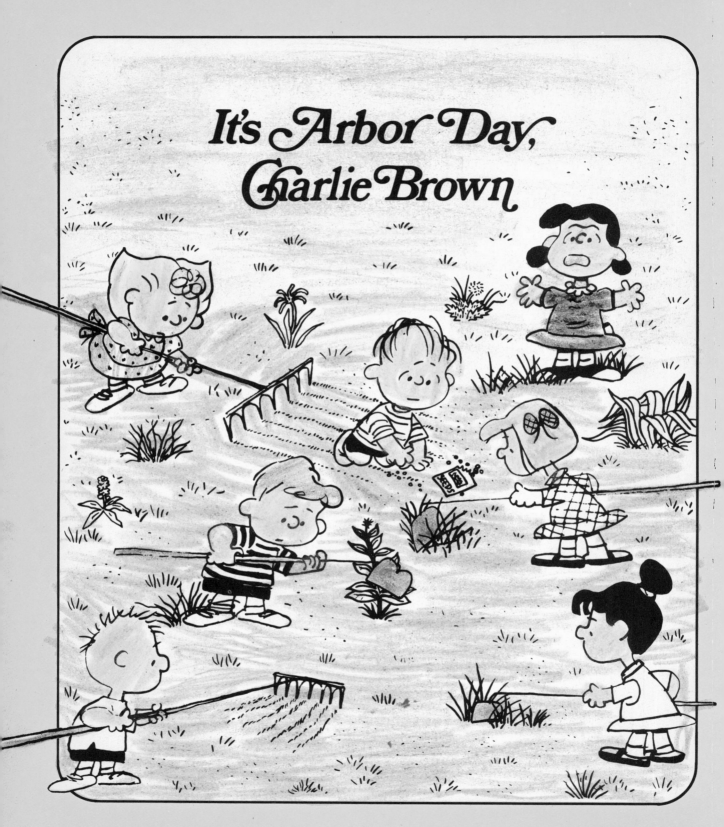

It's Arbor Day, Charlie Brown

What's Arbor Day? That's simple. That's the day
when all the ships come sailing into the arbor.

I've never been so humiliated in all my life! And now the
teacher says I have to give a complete report on Arbor Day.

I found some information on Arbor Day, Sally. "The first Arbor Day was April 10, 1872. Its main idea is that of conservation. Arbor Day points out to both children and adults the need to maintain and protect certain areas of our natural forests and woodlands."

Linus and I have decided to prepare for Arbor Day
by planting some trees. Why don't you join us, Lucy?

Right here is just the place—Charlie Brown's baseball field.
It's got plenty of room and lots of dirt. We might as well put it to
good use. But we'll have to get some stuff from the nursery first.

Hi, Charlie Brown! We've decided to spruce up your old ball field.

Peppermint Patty? It's almost time for the first game of the baseball season. I hope your team can play ours. Our field will be ready, so we can play there.

Glad your field will be in great shape, Chuck, because your team never is.

Lucy, I don't think this
is a good place for the tree.

Nonsense. It will look great.
Let's plant the tree and then get
the whole team to help with the
rest of the field.

O.K., O.K., let's keep it moving. Schroeder, put those rosebushes at third base. Linus, put those geraniums at first and second. Sally, plant those daisies at home plate. Let's go, let's go, let's go!

37

It's time for the first game of the season, Charlie Brown.
And we have a surprise for you at the field.

There it is, Charlie Brown! Happy Arbor Day!

How can anyone pitch with a tree here?

And look at that! A scarecrow!

40

Hey, Chuck, we're here! But what have you done?!
You've got to be mad!

I can't believe I'm pitching from this crazy mound
with a tree on it!

Wow! It's already the third inning, and we're ahead!
I think we're going to win our first game ever!

Hey, Chuck, looks like rain. I guess we'll have to postpone.

Hey, where's everybody going? We can't postpone the game!! We were winning!!

So I'm happy to report that all our trees and plants are doing very well.

I know you're sad 'cause you didn't win. But at least you've got all those pretty trees and plants on your baseball field. Happy Arbor Day, Charlie Brown!

It's The Easter Beagle, Charlie Brown

I'll show you how to color eggs for Easter, Marcie.
You get the eggs ready, and I'll mix up all the colors.

All the eggs are fried, sir. Now how do we color them?

Argh!

Lucy wants you to come to the store with us to get stuff
for Easter—baskets, eggs, candy, the works. But I know that
it's a waste of time. The Easter Beagle will do all that. On
Easter Sunday the Easter Beagle passes colored eggs to all the
good little kids.

Hi, Peppermint Patty! We're here to get stuff for Easter.

Hi, Chuck! Marcie and I are here to get some eggs to color.

It's Easter and they already have the Christmas decorations up! Let's get out of here!

Later . . .

Peppermint Patty said that I'd better boil
the eggs this time.

54

Chuck, I don't know what to do. We've ruined a lot of eggs, and we don't have any colored yet. I've run out of money and can't buy any more eggs. How am I gonna teach my friend here about Easter and coloring eggs when I can't get any more eggs to color.

Don't worry a thing about it. The Easter Beagle will come, and you'll see. He'll bring Easter eggs to all the little kids.

I don't believe in your stupid Easter Beagle, Linus.
Easter is very simple. You paint the eggs. You hide the eggs.
You find the eggs. And you know who's going to find these eggs?
Me! Because I'm the one who's going to hide them!

Well, Marcie. I'm really sorry. Here it is Easter,
and we don't have any colored eggs.

You've done it again, haven't you? I've been waiting here since dawn—waiting for the Easter Beagle. I never learn! Why do I always listen to you? "Trust me," you said. "Trust me! Trust me!" Now I've been burned again!

LOOK!
HE'S COMING!
HE'S COMING!
THE EASTER
BEAGLE IS COMING!
I TOLD YOU HE'D
COME! ! !

Thank you!

Thank you very, very much!

Linus, you were right!
There *is* an Easter Beagle!

Some Easter Beagle!
He gave me my own egg!

Happy Easter, everyone! !

I don't know why it is, Sally, but holidays always depress me.
Do you realize that Thanksgiving is here again?

Hi, Chuck? This is Peppermint Patty. . . .
Listen, I really have a treat for you. My dad's been
called out of town. He said I could come over to your
house and share Thanksgiving dinner with you, Chuck.
And remember that great kid Marcie? Her folks said
it would be O.K. if she joined us. And Franklin can
come, too.

Well . . . I . . .

How do I get into these things?
Peppermint Patty is coming to
Thanksgiving dinner. She's bringing
Marcie and Franklin with her, and
we won't even be home. We'll be at
Grandma's house.

It's your own fault
because you're so
wishy-washy.

What am I going to do, Linus? You can't explain anything to Peppermint Patty because you never get a chance to say anything. Now I'm doomed. She'll hate me for the rest of my life.

Why don't you have *two* dinners? You can cook the first one yourself for your friends, then go to your grandmother's with your family for the second one.

Snoopy, you go out to the garage and get a table that we can set up in the backyard. There are going to be seven of us for Thanksgiving dinner.

Snoopy! How can you serve the food in that ridiculous costume?
Put on your chef's hat. Our guests will be here any minute.

Hi, Chuck. I sure hope we aren't late or anything.
We got here as fast as we could.

In the year 1621 the Pilgrims held their first Thanksgiving feast. They invited the great Indian chief Massasoit, who brought ninety of his brave Indians. Governor William Bradford and Captain Miles Standish were honored guests.

Elder William Brewster, who was a minister, said a prayer that went something like this:

"We thank God for our homes and our food and our safety in a new land. We thank God for the opportunity to create a new world for freedom and justice."

Amen.

A piece of toast! A pretzel stick? Popcorn! . . .
What blockhead cooked all this?
Don't you know *anything* about Thanksgiving, Chuck?

Don't feel bad, Chuck. Peppermint Patty didn't mean all those things she said. Actually, she really likes you.

I don't feel bad for myself. I just feel bad because I ruined everyone's Thanksgiving.

But Thanksgiving is more than eating, Chuck.

Those early Pilgrims were thankful for what had happened to them, and we should be thankful, too. We should just be thankful for being together. I think that's what they mean by Thanksgiving, Charlie Brown.

Apologies accepted, Chuck? There's enough misunderstanding
in the world already without these stupid misunderstandings, Chuck.

Good grief! It's four o'clock. We're supposed to be at Grandma's by four-thirty.

Peppermint Patty, great news. My grandmother says we can all come to her house for Thanksgiving dinner.

So long, Snoop.

A Charlie Brown Christmas

I think there must be something wrong with me, Linus.
Christmas is coming but I'm not happy. I like getting Christmas
cards and all that. But I still end up feeling depressed.

Pig-Pen, I'm glad to see that you enjoy this time
of year. I'm not so lucky.

Some can be content as long as they have food.

What you need, Charlie Brown, is involvement. You should be the director of our Christmas play. Be at the auditorium at three o'clock.

Well, Snoopy, it looks like I'm going to direct the Christmas play.

Big brother, will you please write a letter to Santa Claus for me? I have a long list of presents that I want.

You're much too concerned with presents, Sally. Besides, I have no time now. I'm on my way to the auditorium.

All right! Quiet everybody.
Our director will be here any
minute, and we'll start
rehearsal.

Here is our director, Charlie Brown!

Now the script girl will be handing out your parts.

Frieda and Pig-Pen, you play the innkeeper and his wife.

Shermy, you and Linus are shepherds.

Get rid of that stupid blanket, Linus! ! ! ! What's a Christmas shepherd going to look like holding a stupid blanket like that?

There's something missing from this play. It doesn't have the right spirit. What we need is a Christmas tree.

This really brings
Christmas close to
a person.

Fantastic!

Gee, I didn't know they still
made wooden Christmas trees!

This little green one here
seems to need a home.

Boy, Charlie Brown. What kind of a stupid tree is that?
Why didn't you get an aluminum one? You're hopeless, Charlie
Brown, completely hopeless.

I'm not going to let them spoil my Christmas. I'll take this little tree home and decorate it. I'll show them it really *will* work in our play.

Augh! I've killed it! Everything I touch gets ruined!!

It's not a bad little tree, really.

Maybe it just needs a little love.

What are they doing with Snoopy's decorations?

You'll see.

MERRY CHRISTMAS, CHARLIE BROWN!

Happy Holidays, Charlie Brown!